THE SEAR

Eric Heuvel | Ruud van der Rol | Lies Schippers

THE SEARCH

*A graphic novel of courage and resistance
brought to you by the Anne Frank House*

MACMILLAN CHILDREN'S BOOKS

Esther's parents,
Dr. and Mrs. Hecht

Esther

Helena van Dort

Bob's parents,
Mr. and Mrs. Canter

Bob

Esther and her grandson, Daniel

Helena and her grandson, Jeroen

Bob

Esther's son, Paul, lives in
the Netherlands. Esther is visiting from
the United States to celebrate her grandson Daniel's
Bar Mitzvah. She also wants to spend time with her
long-lost friend Helena and introduce Daniel to
Helena's grandson, Jeroen.

19

...PREPARE FOR TRANSPORT...

My parents were also taken away.

Esther! She's still at school!

Schneller! Faster!

Then they saw Helena's father. He had been dispatched to help the Germans.

Look!

Our neighbor!

Nazi!

Keep moving!

Esther's at school. Help us?!

I'll see what I can do.

The neighbors stood by...

We can't help them.

Where are they being taken?

To the Dutch Theatre.

32

34

Farewell letters were thrown from the train. People who lived in the area often mailed them.

Dear Aunt and Uncle. We're on the train. We're very brave. So please don't worry. We have no idea where we're headed. Betty and Jacob.

How long is the trip?

I can't breathe!

No idea...

Don't push!

Careful! It's hard for her to stand.

Sit on these suitcases.

A day later...

The pail is full. The stench...

It can't be much longer.

After a while...

Empty the pails! Fetch water!

This isn't nearly over...

They were robbed on the way.

Your money and jewelry!

SCHNELL!

Three days later, everyone was totally exhausted.

So now what's next?

They were on their way to Auschwitz, a Nazi death camp in occupied Poland.

The reality of what had gone on in eastern Europe only became clear after the war.

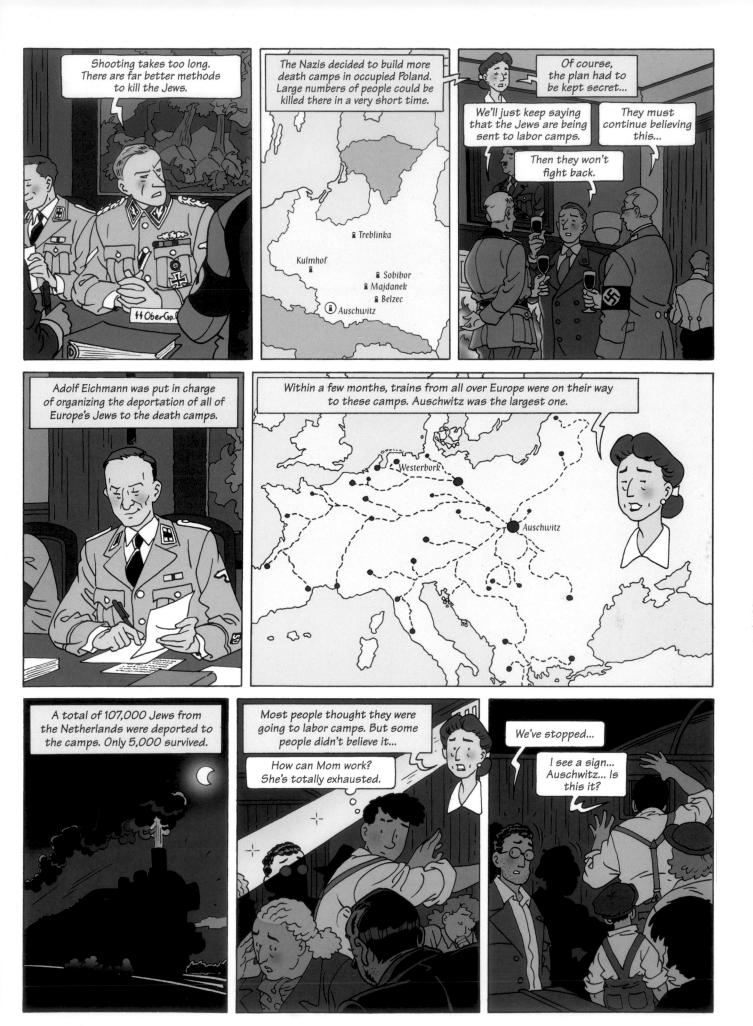

Day and night, Bob saw the smoking chimneys.

Auschwitz-Birkenau had several gas chambers.

1. Gas chambers and crematoria
2. "Canada Commando"
3. Gas chambers and crematoria
4. Women's camp
5. Infirmary
6. Roma and Sinti
7. Men's camp
8. Medical experiments
9. Entrance gate
10. Train platform

Camp under construction

SS barracks

Bob ended up in the men's camp with other Jews and also political prisoners, mainly from Poland and Russia.

To są Holendrzy...*

*They're from Holland.

Auschwitz-Birkenau was also a labor camp. The Nazis wanted the prisoners to work themselves to death.

What were they forced to do?

Well, a bit of everything... building roads, working in a munitions factory, building barracks...

The day began before dawn at 4 a.m.

Wake up! Roll call! Schnell, schneller!!!

First the prisoners were counted. They often stood for hours.

Then the real work would begin. Bob and our fathers had to lug heavy stones.

Son, I won't make it!

If you quit, they'll shoot you!

55

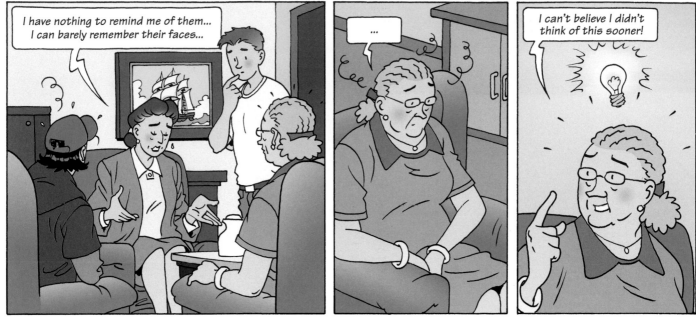

59

The Search was originally published in Dutch in 2007 by the Anne Frank House in cooperation with the Jewish Historical Museum of Amsterdam under the title *De Zoektocht*

This edition is published in agreement with the Anne Frank House

This edition published 2011 by Macmillan Children's Books
a division of Macmillan Publishers Limited
20 New Wharf Road, London N1 9RR
Basingstoke and Oxford
Associated companies throughout the world
www.panmacmillan.com

ISBN 978-0-330-51976-2

Scenario
Eric Heuvel
Ruud van der Rol
Lies Schippers
Drawings
Eric Heuvel/Redhill Illustrations
Translated from the Dutch by
Lorraine T. Miller (Epicycles, Amsterdam)
Coloring
J & M Colorstudio
Creative Support and Documentation
Jacqueline Koerts/Redhill Illustrations
Design
Karel Oosting, Amsterdam
Production
Anne Frank House, Amsterdam

A special thank-you goes to Annemiek Gringold (Hollandsche Schouwburg/Dutch Theatre Memorial Centre) for contributing her expertise in the development of the scenario.

The Search was originally published in Dutch as *De Zoektocht*, thanks in part to funding provided by the Ministry of Public Health, Welfare and Sport (VWS) in the Netherlands.

Many others also offered their comments and advice in the development of the scenario:

Content Experts (The Netherlands)
R. C. Musaph-Andriesse (Advisory Council, Anne Frank House)
Liesbeth van der Horst (Dutch Resistance Museum, Amsterdam)
Dirk Mulder, Erik Guns (Memorial Center Camp Westerbork)
Nine Nooter (National Committee May 4th and 5th)
René Kok, Erik Somers (Netherlands Institute for War Documentation/NIOD)
Jeroen van der Eijnde (National Monument Camp Vught)
Femke Akerboom (Markt 12 Museum, Aalten)
Ido Abram (Learning Foundation, Amsterdam)
Joost van Bodegom (Chairman Resistance Museum)
Joël Cahen, Petra Katzenstein, Léontine Meijer (Jewish Historical Museum, Amsterdam)
Menno Metselaar, Marian Stegeman, Mieke Sobering (Anne Frank House)

Content Experts (International)
Paul Salmons (Imperial War Museum, Great Britain)
Wolf Kaiser (Wannsee Conference House Memorial, Germany)
Claude Singer and Philippe Boukara (Shoah Memorial, France)
Mirosław Obstarczyk (Auschwitz State Museum, Poland)
Piotr Trojanski (German-Polish Center, Poland)
Monica Kovács (Hannah Arendt Association, Hungary)
Werner Dreier (National Socialism and the Holocaust: Memory and Present, Austria)

Another graphic novel of courage and resistance brought to you by the Anne Frank House:

Eric Heuvel

A FAMILY SECRET

While searching his grandmother's attic for likely items to sell at a yard sale, Jeroen finds a scrapbook his grandmother Helena made during the Second World War. It brings back painful memories for her, and she tells Jeroen for the first time about her experiences as a girl living in Amsterdam during the German occupation of the Netherlands and about the loss of her Jewish best friend, Esther. But after hearing the story, Jeroen makes a surprising discovery.

In this gripping, historically accurate graphic novel, ordinary people in different roles – from victim to bystander to collaborator to perpetrator – make the most difficult, important decisions of their lives.